MW01079419

THE WEAPONS EN

TANK AIRCRAFT AFV SHIP ARTILLERY VEHICLES SECRET WEAPON

TWE-012 EN

MEDIUM TANK M11/39

THE WEAPONS ENCYCLOPÆDIA

EDITORIAL STAFF

Luca Cristini, Paolo Crippa.

CONTRIBUTORS

Enrico Acerbi, Massimiliano Afiero, Aldo Antonicelli, Ruggero Calò, Luigi Carretta, Flavio Chistè, Anna Cristini, Carlo Cucut, Salvo Fagone, Enrico Finazzer, Björn Huber, Andrea Lombardi, Aymeric Lopez, Marco Lucchetti, Luigi Manes, Giovanni Maressi, Francesco Mattesini, Federico Peirani, Alberto Peruffo, Maurizio Raggi, Andrea Alberto Tallillo, Antonio Tallillo, Massimo Zorza.

PUBLISHED BY

Luca Cristini Editore (Soldiershop), via Orio, 35/4 - 24050 Zanica (BG) ITALY.

DISTRIBUTION BY

Soldiershop - www.soldiershop.com, Amazon, Ingram Spark, Berliner Zinnfigurem (D), LaFeltrinelli, Mondadori, Libera Editorial (Spain), Google book (eBook), Kobo, (eBoook), Apple Book (eBook).

CONTRIBUTORS OF THIS VOLUME & ACKNOWLEDGEMENTS

We would like to thank the main contributors to this issue: The profiles of the floats are all by the author. The colouring of the photos is by Anna Cristini. Special thanks to national and/or private institutions such as: Army General Staff, State Archives, Bundesarchiv, Nara, Library of Congress etc. To P.Crippa, A.Lopez, L.Manes, C.Cucut, Tallillo archives. Model Victoria (www.modelvictoria.it), for providing images or other items from their archives.

For a complete list of Soldiershop titles, or for every information please contact us on our website: www.soldiershop.com or www. cristinieditore.com. E-mail: info@soldiershop.com. Keep up to date on Facebook & Twitter: https://www.facebook.com/soldiershop. publishing

Title: **ITALIAN MEDIUM TANK M11/39** Code.: **TWE-012 EN**
Series by L. S. Cristini
ISBN code: 978-88-93279925. First edition July 2023
THE WEAPONS ENCYCLOPAEDIA (SOLDIERSHOP) is a trademark of Luca Cristini Editore

THE WEAPONS ENCYCLOPÆDIA
TANK AIRCRAFT AFV SHIP ARTILLERY VEHICLES SECRET WEAPON

ITALIAN MEDIUM TANK M11/39

LUCA STEFANO CRISTINI

BOOK SERIES FOR MODELERS & COLLECTORS

SOLDIERSHOP PUBLISHING
ILLUSTRATEDHISTORY

CONTENTS

Introduction 5

- Development and project 5

- Technical characteristics 8

Operational use 23

- First major deployment in A.O.I. (Italian Eastern Africa) 23

- North Africa 24

- Italy 30

- Conclusion 33

Camouflage and distinguishing marks 41

Production and export 47

Data sheet 52

Bibliography..58

▼ M11/39 runs across the sand of the Libyan desert near the Egyptian border near Sidi el Barrani, 1940. This and many other images belong to the state archive.

INTRODUCTION

The M11/39 was a medium tank employed by the Royal Army at the beginning of World War II, specifically from 1939 to 1940. This tank marked a transitional phase between the tracked vehicles and the M13/40, paving the way for the subsequent family of medium tanks used throughout the conflict.

This tank, which Marshal Badoglio described as 'magnificent', undoubtedly represented a step forward compared to the models then in use by our armoured units, but some design shortcomings marked its meteoric decline.

In fact, the M11/39 had several critical issues to deal with. Its undersized engine, cannon positioned inside a box and lack of radio equipment were the main challenges to overcome. Moreover, it was not optimised for desert combat, with the limitations and tactics specific to that region.

Despite these shortcomings, the M11/39 marked an important step forward in the evolution of Italy's armoured capabilities, laying the foundation for later developments in the field of tanks.

▉ DEVELOPMENT AND PROJECT

The idea of developing a combat tank emerged in 1932, when an 8-tonne vehicle was conceived that eventually evolved into the final prototype known as the M11/39, presented by Ansaldo in 1937. The M11/39 can be considered the first Italian medium tank, weighing 11 tonnes, equipped with a 37 mm cannon mounted in a casemate and two 8 mm Breda Mod. 38 machine guns in the turret. Armouring ranged from 8 mm (hull, engine bulkheads, turret top) to 30 mm (turret and plates around the gun), with the sides and front of the hull protected by 14.5 mm armour. During combat operations, both the armament and armour proved inadequate against the medium and heavy tanks used by the Allies. De-

▲ M11/39 tank fresh off the production lines of Ansaldo's factories and photographed in the company's premises. Courtesy Ansaldo archive. Author's colouring.

spite this, the M11/39 was used with moderate success against light tanks, machine gun emplacements, bunkers and enemy trenches. Overall, however, the tank did not meet the requirements, with its main limitations including limited armament, insufficient armour, low engine power and general mechanical weakness. In addition, the 37 mm cannon was mounted in a fixed casemate instead of a rotating turret, forcing the tank to turn completely around to aim. The hull of this tank was used as the basis for later Italian medium tanks such as the M13/40, M14/41 and M15/42. The diesel engine had an output of 105 hp, which was increased to 125 hp in the next model, the M13/40.

After several experiments and evaluations of foreign tanks, Italy decided to focus on creating a tank suitable for mountain warfare and colonial use instead of one specifically designed to fight contemporary European tanks. This led to a delay in the production of the first modern Italian tank equipped with a cannon.

In 1936, the Italian Army issued requirements for a tank with a crew of three, armed with a 37 mm L40 cannon mounted in the hull and two 8 mm machine guns in the turret. This new vehicle was intended to replace the old Fiat 3000 tanks still in service along with the CV.3 light tanks. Although an initial prototype was built in 1936, it was abandoned the following year.

In May 1938, the Italian Army officially decided that tanks with guns would be essential for the new composition of armoured divisions.

Production of the M11/39 began in 1938, with an output of 9 units per month. However, in December 1939, the entire Italian medium tank production was concentrated on the M13/40, as the M11/39 was deemed to be a failure. Consequently, the M11/39 assembly line was closed.

In total, 100 examples of the M11/39 were produced. According to another source, that of Giulio Benussi, three pre-series and 70 series were built. According to others, 90 tanks were built.

▲ M11/39 tank tested for its operational capabilities at a Royal Army training camp. State Archives.

M11/39 MEDIUM TANK IN ITALY, AUTUMN 1939

▲ M11/39 of the 2nd Company 1st Battalion Medium Tank, Italy, autumn 1939.
In the small photo the same tank engaged in rough terrain testing on a national field.

▲ The M11 tank presented to the Duce, who seems as enthusiastic about the vehicle as the two hierarchs in orbaceous clothing accompanying it.

■ TECHNICAL CHARACTERISTICS

The M11/39 was a tank that was assembled primarily through riveting, with limited use of welding due to the lack of skilled labour. The rivets used to fasten the armour plates were hexagonal with conical heads, designed to reduce the risk of breakage when hit by small-calibre bullets.

The internal configuration of the vehicle included the transmission and gearbox at the front, followed by the cockpit with seats for the driver and gunner. The tank commander sat in the turret. For access to the fuel tank, there were several options: a hatch on the left side of the cockpit, a hatch above the gun or a hatch on the turret.

On the front deck, near the brakes, were two inspection hatches. On the rear deck were two maintenance hatches for the 105 hp diesel engine, located behind the cockpit. To the left of the engine was the main fuel tank, while to the right was the reserve tank. The two engine fans were protected by ventilation grilles located at the rear of the engine bonnet.

The partition wall between the engine compartment and the cockpit/combat chamber was perforated to allow the passage of the clutch, from which the drive shaft exited, connecting it to the gearbox.

The driver had four gears plus reverse gear. The undercarriage consisted of a front sprocket, a rear tension wheel, two bogies with four twin rollers each and three upper support rollers. The all-metal tracks consisted of 84 links each. The suspension, designed to cope with mountainous terrain, was efficient and reliable, but the tank was plagued by fragile mechanical transmission components and an underpowered engine, which limited its performance. This was reflected in the frequent breakdowns and widespread poor reliability of the vehicle.

In terms of optical instrumentation, the tank was equipped with a panoramic periscope mounted on the turret, which allowed a 360-degree view with a 30-degree field of view. The episcope provided the pilot with minimal visibility when the hatch had to be closed. For weapon aiming, there were two sights with a 30-degree field of view: one located to the left of the gun, with the peculiarity that only the lens followed the elevation movement of the weapon, and the other positioned between the two machine guns on the turret.

The Vickers-Terni 37/40 cannon mounted in the body of the M11/39 tank had a limited rotation capability of 30 degrees and could be elevated or lowered between -8 and +12 degrees. The gun could be aimed manually or by means of a hydraulic motor, while the elevation had to be adjusted manually. Mounted on the turret were two 8mm Breda Model 38 machine guns, which were fed by 117 magazines containing 24 rounds each.

The M11/39 tank had a crew of three. The commander was in the small single-seat turret at the top of the

▲ Beautiful front view of the M11/39 tank in camouflage. State Archives.

vehicle, the gunner occupied the right front position of the hull and the driver was at the left front. The turret was offset approximately 30 cm to the left of the vehicle's centreline and had an internal diameter of only 876.3 mm. Access to the interior of the vehicle was via a hatch in the roof of the hull.

However, the internal ergonomics of the tank were not optimal. The interior height was limited, which prevented the commander from standing fully upright, and there were risks to the commander from the recoil of the cannon. The interior environment of the vehicle was quite uncomfortable and potentially dangerous for the crew.

Inside the vehicle, the pilot was on the left, the gunner on the right and the tank leader occupied the turret. The tank leader gave orders verbally, while the gunner used a telescope with 1x magnification. The pilot had a slit for vision, while the gunship leader could use a telescope and a periscope with 1x magnification. Communication inside and outside the vehicle was limited, and commands were given verbally or via flags.

The armour plating of the M11/39 consisted of steel plates bolted together. During hull production, the armour plates were connected using countersunk hexagonal head bolts. This method of assembly allowed flexibility and facilitated the repair and replacement of damaged plates. However, several reports were made about possible problems in the production of the armour, particularly for the turret.

The M11/39 employed a 90-degree V-shaped Fiat SPA diesel engine with 8 cylinders (2 valves per cylinder) and a displacement of 11.14 litres. Despite having an output of only 105 hp, the engine was initially considered a strong point of the vehicle. Some sources report an increased output of 125 hp, which may represent theoretical rather than actual performance. The engine structure comprised aluminium cylinder blocks and crankcase, with detachable cylinder heads. According to engineer Sir Harry Ricardo, Fiat's pre-war consultant, the design could have achieved a maximum output of 150 hp using its patented Comet head.

▲ View of the engine being assembled in Ansaldo's factories. State Archives/Ansaldo.

The engine was powered by a FIAT injection pump, and there were two fuel filters. The engine speed regulator was mounted next to the injection pump shaft.

Lubrication of the dry sump type was achieved by three pumps housed close to the engine sump. The oil required for this lubrication was approximately 14 litres.

In one of the models captured from the enemy that was later examined, a report was written by the British MI10 responsible for studying the vehicle, and when the engine was analysed, it was found to be very complicated due to the fact that the vehicle had suffered a serious fire and had subsequently arrived damaged and corroded by rust. Therefore, the actual condition of the engine during the analysis may have been compromised.

The engine compartment of the M11/39 housed two fuel tanks: a main tank and a reserve tank positioned above the engine, with the air filters above them and the radiator at the rear. The main tank had a capacity of about 150 litres, while the reserve tank held about 40 litres. However, due to the long distances involved in desert fighting in 1940, some M11/39 vehicles were equipped with an additional 23-litre external tank. Altogether, the 190 litres of fuel allowed an operational range of about 10 hours or 200 km, while the additional 23-litre tank increased the range to about 11 hours or 222 km.

The cooling air flow for the engine was through an air intake at the rear of the fighting compartment. Air was drawn in from that area and directed towards the engine compartment, also providing ventilation for the crew. Air was also sucked in through slits in the engine compartment doors.

The transmission of the M11/39 consisted of a four-speed box with a reverse gear, located at the front of the vehicle. A particularly positive aspect of the tank was the possibility of starting the engine either from the outside via a crank or from inside the vehicle. The British considered this feature very attractive and seriously considered it for advantageous adoption in their future designs.

▲ View of the idler system of the M11/39. State Archives/Ansaldo.

▲ Interior of the cockpit-combat chamber of the M11 medium tank.

▼ Individual tank equipment, from the original 1939 manual.

DOTAZIONE INDIVIDUALE

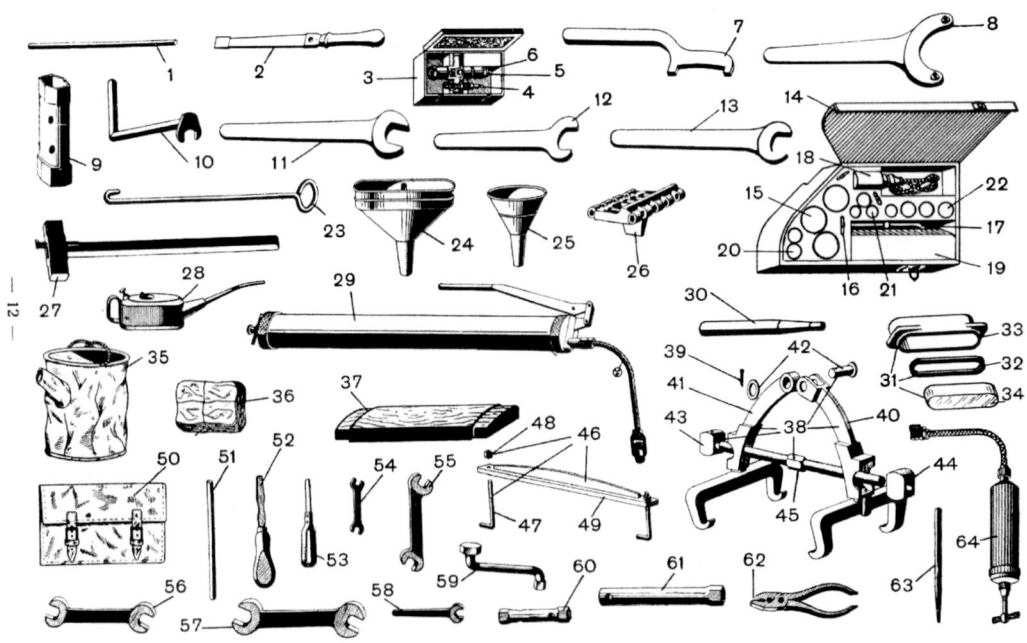

DOTAZIONE INDIVIDUALE

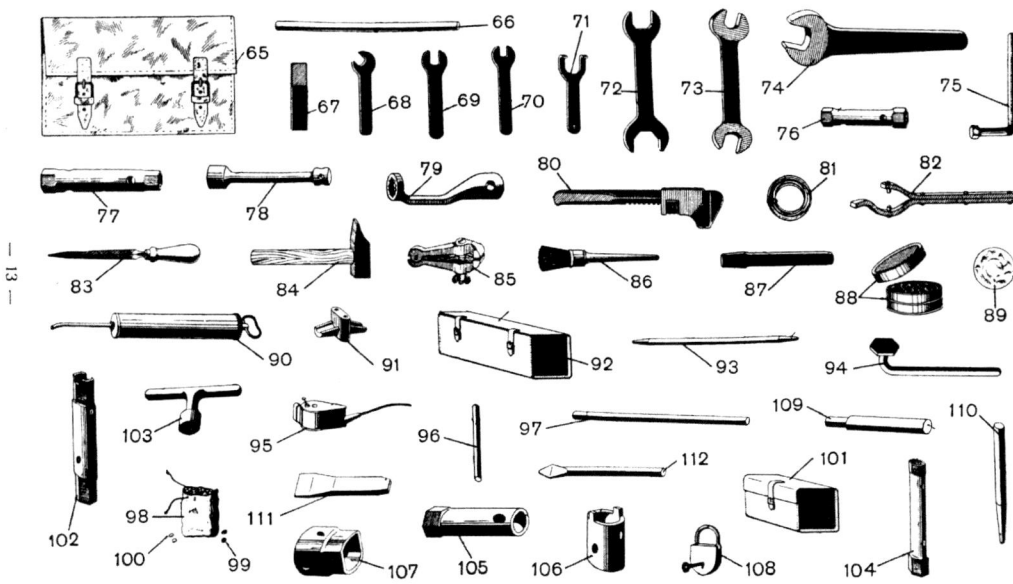

▲ ▼ Individual tank equipment, from the original 1939 manual.

DOTAZIONE DI SQUADRA

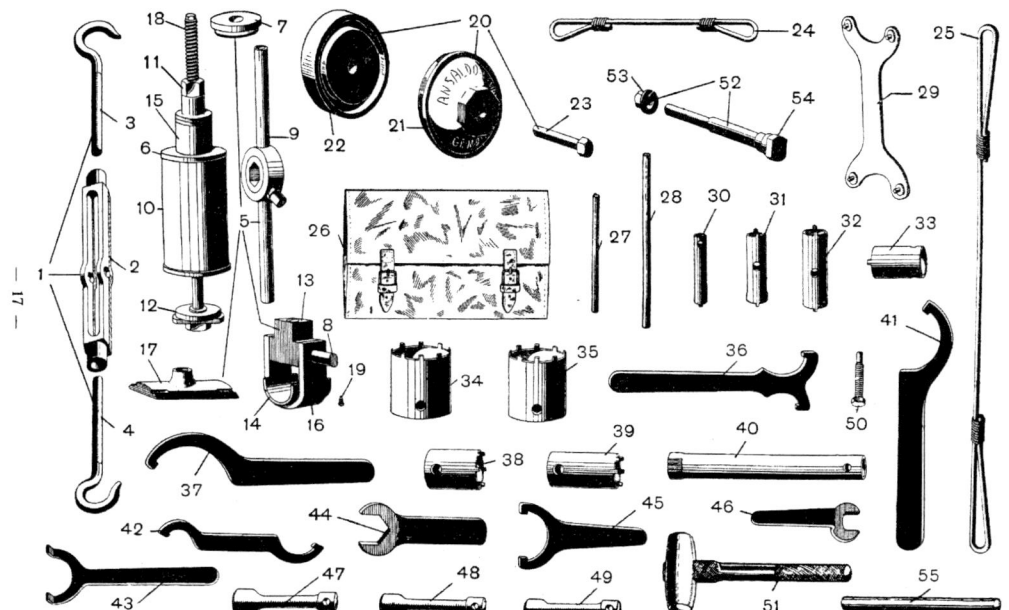

In terms of suspension, the M11/39 had two suspension groups on each side of the vehicle, with four wheels in each group. The wheels had a diameter of 30 cm and used tyres supplied by Pirelli. The track was supported by 3 tyred deflection rollers, also from Pirelli, with a diameter of 240 mm. The suspension springs consisted of 10 laminated lamellas, with no shock absorbers. The track, 260 mm wide and made of pressed steel parts, had 80 links on each side. The production of the track required several processing steps, which was also very interesting from the point of view of the analyses carried out by the enemy on captured vehicles.

Track tension was via an adjusting nut mounted on an arm connected to the rear idler wheel, while transmission to the track was via a double drive sprocket positioned at the front. The oft-cited British study of the vehicle rated the suspension as particularly strong, but they found that it was, however, too vulnerable to damage, with the very annoying possibility that a single wheel damage could immobilise the vehicle.

In terms of armament, the M11/39 was equipped with a twin system of machine guns mounted on a small turret and a main gun in the hull. The machine guns were mounted on a gimbal that allowed them to be turned and lowered a few degrees independently of the turret. The main gun was a 37 Mm Vickers-Terni. It was an old model produced at the Terni factory in Italy. Despite its age, the cannon was light and compact, weighing only 95 kg. It had a falling wedge breech with a single hydraulic recoil pad mounted above it. Sights for the cannon included a telescope and a graduated open sight for different distances. The spatial movement of the cannon was limited to only 30 degrees, while the elevation could vary from -8 to +12 degrees. This manoeuvre could be manual or hydraulic, while the elevation was manual only. The ammunition for the main cannon was stored in boxes placed under the cannon, with a total of 84 rounds carried. In addition, 117 24-round magazines for the machine guns were carried inside the tank, totalling 2,808 rounds. The hydraulic gun handling system was considered very good by the British, who found it compact, simple and effective. They were so impressed by this Italian system that

▲ Another interesting view of the interior of the cockpit-combat chamber of the M11 medium tank. Archive Ansaldo.

they sought another cannon for further testing. However, they were also puzzled by the fact that such a small cannon required a hydraulic crosshead, assuming that the crosshead mount could have friction and was not supported by roller or ball bearings.

The choice of the 37 mm Vickers-Terni cannon had caused production problems, as supplies of this cannon were slow. Some cannon had to be taken from Fiat 3000 vehicles to fulfil the order for M11-39s. This reason combined with the fact that it was still too light a calibre to compete with its contemporary enemy tanks, together with the poor cannon and too weak armour led to the failure of the entire project.

Regarding the cannon, the insistence on the Vickers-Terni anyway suggests that a cannon with a calibre greater than 40 mm was not selected simply because it would have been too heavy to handle.

Let us complete our analysis of the tank by talking about the electrical equipment provided on board. This was provided by a set of four 6-volt batteries, all connected together in series, a dynamo, two starter motors, and eight spark plugs. An external lighting system comprised two 50-watt front lights and a rear light to illuminate the number plate.

For the interior, four or five 5-watt bulbs were used to illuminate the combat chamber and dashboard. The tank was also equipped with a Marelli RF-1-CA two-way radio (source: Giulio Benussi).

This was enclosed in a bonnet placed inside the tank on the right side, This radio had the following features:

Transmitter: with a frequency range of 11/9 metres, 10 watts output power. Modulation depth 70/80%.

Receiver: with frequency range 11/9 metres, selectivity at 25 kc 40 db and output power 2 watts. Modulation depth 70/80%. This equipment could receive and transmit in both morse and speech.

▲ Very well defined detail of the turret and weapon system of the M11/39 tank. Ansaldo Archive.

▲ Various pictures of the tests carried out on the M11/39 tank (State Archives).

▲ Italian M11/39 tank column in training in an Italian village before the entry into the war.

▲ Transceiver system supplied on board the M11/39 tank (according to Giulio Benussi).

M11/39 MEDIUM TANK IN ITALIAN EAST AFRICA (A.O.I.), 1940

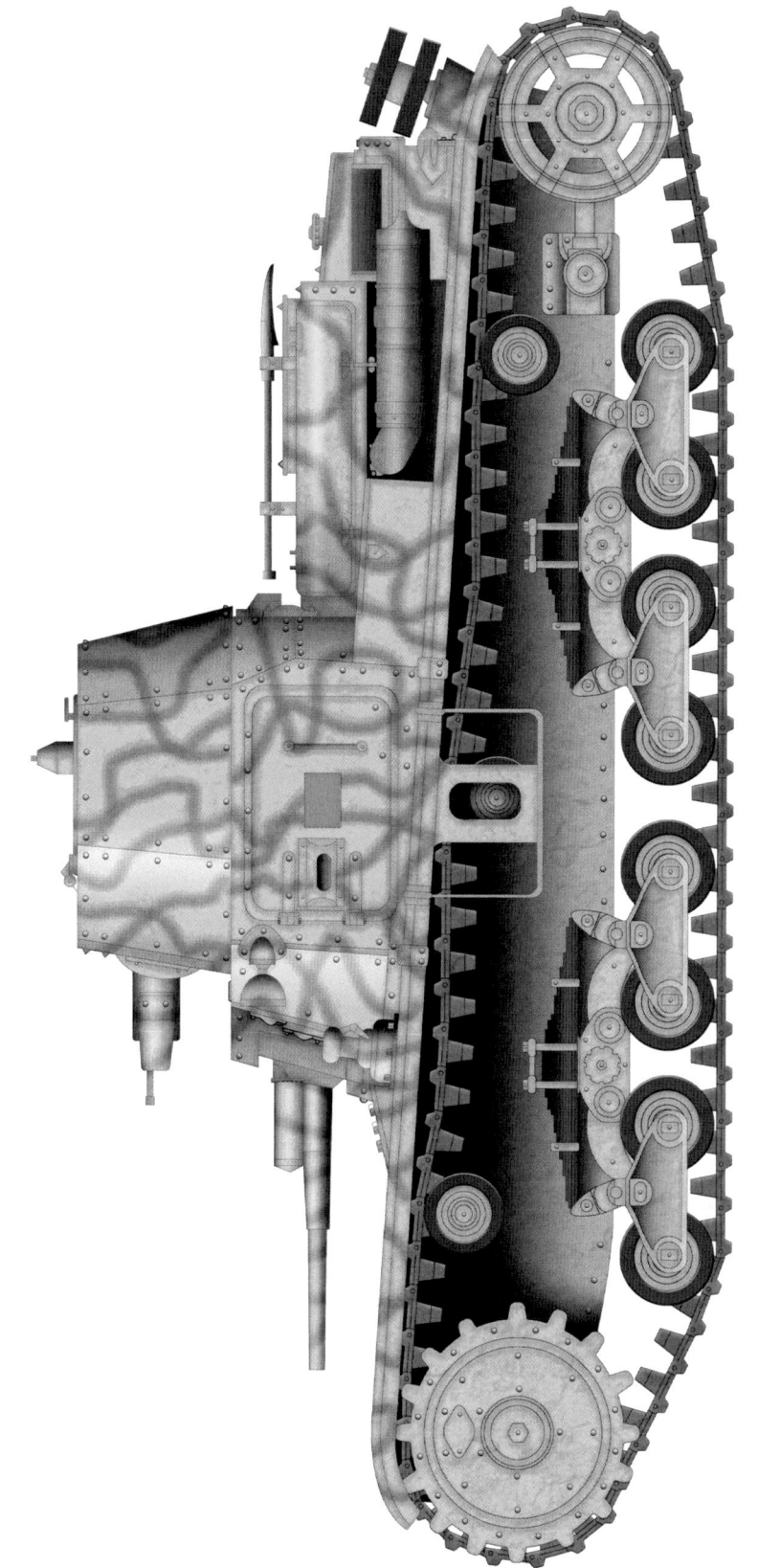

▲ M11/39 of the 4th M Group Company in Italian East Africa (Ethiopia) in 1940.

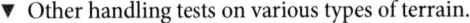

▲ Test runs of the first M11 medium wagon made in Piedmont in 1939.

▼ Other handling tests on various types of terrain.

M11/39 MEDIUM TANK IN LIBYA IN 1940

▲ M11/39 of an armoured group in North Africa in 1940.
In the small photo the same M11/39 tank of the 1st Tank Battalion in Cyrenaica in 1940.

► Curious patriotic colouring of this M11/39 with a tricolour Italian flag decorating the high turret (see profile on page 25). Command soon realised that this was not a good idea, and that it operated at the exact opposite of the principles of camouflage. Africa 1940.

► The medium Italian tank ended up in the hands of the enemy on more than one occasion, mostly to Australian or British troops. This was not the case with this one, which was instead captured by South African troops in A.O.I. and immediately decorated with a curious crown of huge 'ones' painted on the turret. See profile page 55.

▲ This Italian tank driver who died next to his M11 is a plastic demonstration of the disaster that befell the Italian troops in isolated Italian East Africa.

OPERATIONAL USE

S tarting in 1939, the year of its substantial entry into service, at the outbreak of war the M11/39 medium tank was mainly used on African soil, both in Libya and in Italian East Africa. After the abandonment of Tunisia, only four M11 tanks were still present in the metropolitan area. Of these, one was employed by units of the RSI and another, captured by the Germans, was used by them in the days of September 1943 in Rome.

◼ FIRST MAJOR DEPLOYMENT IN A.O.I. (ITALIAN EASTERN AFRICA)

Of the first 96 M11/39 tanks produced, 24 M11/39 tanks (12 deployed in Eritrea and 12 in Ethiopia) were sent to Italian East Africa (A.O.I.) in late April and early May 1940, shortly before Italy's entry into the war, to reinforce the armoured units of this colony, isolated from France after the declaration of war, while another 72 were sent to Libya in July 1940 to fight against British forces. These tanks came from the $2^{nd}/32^{nd}$ Battalion, which explains the disparity in numbers between the two battalions sent to Libya. The M11/39s deployed in East Africa were divided into two companies, 321st and 322nd , divided into four platoons with 12 tanks per company. Both units participated in the capture of Kassala in British Somaliland on 4 July 1940, while 321st company was destroyed at Agordat, west of Keren, at the end of March 1941.

In the first battle on 5 August 1940 at Sidi Azez, the Italian forces destroyed two British tanks and captured two others, but lost three M11/39s. In November 1940, during an attempt to break out of a British encirclement at Alam el Quatrani, five of the 27 M11-39s still operational were lost or knocked out of action.

▲ A column of M11/39 tanks, armed with a Vickers-Terni 37/40 main gun and a twin 8 mm Breda machine gun turret, moving towards Berbera after the Battle of Tug Argan in British Somaliland, 15 August 1940, during the Italian East African Campaign in Somalia.

The 322nd company participated in the invasion of British Somalia in August 1940. However, after the retreat to Harar, it was reduced to 10 tanks in April 1941 and disbanded on 22 May. During the fighting, some tanks were captured by the Allies, including one captured by South African troops.

Due to their limited numbers, they were never used on a large scale and the lack of spare parts, which were mainly available in North Africa, soon rendered them unusable.

This was unfortunate considering that they could have played a crucial role in Libya in slowing down the advance of the British forces.

Some of the tanks sent to North and East Africa were repainted with a two-tone camouflage scheme with sharp edges, retaining the dark green colour but adding a yellow ochre tint. This camouflage scheme appears to have been inspired by the colours used on aeroplanes, as Saharan khaki was not yet in use at the time. Some captured M11-39s were later painted with large white kangaroos by Australian forces and put into service against Italian forces. The Australians organised them into three companies called *Dingo*, *Wombat* and *Rabbit*.

■ NORTH AFRICA

In July 1940, the Italian army had 72 M11-39s in Libya, which had been ceded by the 'Ariete' Division. However, the use of M11-39s in this context was mainly limited to small actions to counter British attacks. Some of them took part in the occupation of Sidi el Barrani. During the British counter-offensive in the winter of 1940-1941, 24 M11-39s assigned to the Maletti Regiment were confronted by a force of 47 British Matilda tanks, whose armour proved impenetrable to the small 37mm guns of the M11-39s. This led to the almost total destruction of the Italian armoured contingent. Later, some M11/39 units captured by Australian troops during Operation *Compass* were re-used by them in operations at Tobruk in 1941.

▲ M11/39 tanks of the 321st company, captured by the British at Agordat, Eritrea 1941 (author's colour).

M11/39 MEDIUM TANK IN NORTH AFRICA IN 1940

▲ M11/39 of an armoured group in North Africa in 1940.

In the small photo the post-combat photo of the M11/39 crew showing that painting the large Italian tricolour on the turret, used as a sign of recognition in June 1940, turned out to be a bad idea.

▲ M11/39 tanks captured by Australian troops in the Tobruk theatre, Libya (author's colouring).

▲ M11/39 tanks captured and immediately reused by Australian troops in Africa (author's colouring).

M11/39 MEDIUM TANK IN EGYPT IN 1940

▲ M11/39 of the Ariete Division, 4th Tank Regiment, 3rd tanks of the 2nd Platoon of the 1st Company, Egypt, September 1940.

M11/39 MEDIUM TANK IN AFRICA IN 1940

▲ M11/39 belonging to the Littorio Division, Africa 1940.

When Italy entered the war, the 32ⁿᵈ Ariete Regiment was equipped with several of the 100 M11-39s produced. The I/32ⁿᵈ battalion, with three companies, and two companies of the II/32ⁿᵈ battalion were sent to Libya, totalling 72 tanks. Upon arrival in Benghazi between 8 and 9 July 1940, they were placed under the command of the 4ᵗʰ Tank Infantry Regiment.

One of the two companies of the 2ⁿᵈ Battalion was immediately detached to join the Maletti Regiment. The M11 faced its first combat in North Africa on 5 August, when a company of the 1ˢᵗ Battalion clashed with British tanks at Sidi Azeiz. During this action, two tanks were destroyed and two captured, while three M11s suffered damage.

Mechanical failures were frequent in the desert due to the long road marches, rocky terrain and fine dust, which limited the effective operation of the M11-39s deployed in North Africa.

During Graziani's offensive in Egypt in September 1940, Battalion I was assigned to XXIII Army Corps, while Battalion II, with the exception of the company detached to the Maletti Regiment, was assigned to the Libyan Divisions Group. On 5 November, the 2ⁿᵈ Battalion was sent to Alam el Quatrani to support the 2ⁿᵈ Libyan Division in breaking the encirclement orchestrated by British tanks. During the 19 November battle at Alam Abou Hileimat, the 1ˢᵗ Battalion lost five of its 27 operational tanks. Subsequently, on 25 November, the 1ˢᵗ Battalion was incorporated into the Special Armoured Brigade.

However, the 2ⁿᵈ Battalion suffered another crushing defeat on 9 December at the start of the British

▲ M11/39 tanks during the counteroffensive in the Cyrenaica desert, which led to the recovery of a large part of Libya, which had been lost at the beginning of the conflict during Rodolfo Graziani's campaign.

offensive. It was completely annihilated by the Matilda tanks of the 7th Royal Tank Regiment at Nibeiwa, and 6 of its tanks were later used by the 6th Australian Cavalry Regiment, which painted large white kangaroos on the flanks and turret of the tanks for their visual recognition. The 1st Battalion, during the capture of Tobruk in January 1941, was also destroyed, as most of the remaining 32 M11s were no longer operational with a critical shortage of spare parts. Finally, in January 1941, only five M11-39s were still operational for the Italian forces in North Africa, but these too were later lost at El Adem on 21 January. Upon returning to Italy after abandoning the last defence of Tunisia, the Regio Esercito was unable to save even one M11/39 tank.

■ ITALY

On 28 July 1939, the CCCXXII/32nd M Tank Battalion in Vicenza received the first M11/39 tanks. During important manoeuvres in Piedmont in August 1939, a company of the 32nd regiment tested the twelve pre-production units. At the end of these exercises, positive comments were reported on the new armoured vehicle, although the need to place the gun in the turret was evident.

After the loss of Africa and close to September 1943 and the armistice with the Allies, only four M11s remained in Italy, three of which were used for training purposes in cavalry schools, while the last one was assigned to the CSM (Centre for Military Studies) where it was partially dismantled for teaching purposes. During the aforementioned confusion in Italy due to the armistice, during the attempted defence of Rome by the Italian army, a surviving M11 tank was captured by German troops and reused by them on this occasion (see profile on page 56).

The last M11/39 to appear on a war front was used in Piedmont during the war of liberation by the National Republican Army (from the GNR) During Operation *Nachtigal* in the Pinerolo area in July 1944, the XIII Marcello Turchinetti Black Brigade temporarily used an M11/39 on loan from the cavalry school. After this operation, the tank was abandoned (see profile on page 57).

▲ M11/39 tanks marching towards Sidi el Barrani, during Rodolfo Graziani's campaign.

M11/39 MEDIUM TANK IN NORTH AFRICA IN 1940

▲ M11/39 FIAT-Ansaldo in North Africa 1940.

▲ Uniform of the Italian tank drivers 1940-1943. Artwork by the author.

■ CONCLUSION

The M11/39 was a tank with unusual characteristics. The decision to place the main armament in the hull was a practical solution for transporting the cannon, but proved ill-suited for combat in the vast North African desert. The limitations of the cannon's movement due to its position compromised the vehicle's effectiveness, despite the use of a good hydraulic system. In addition, the lack of a standard tank radio further aggravated its lateral movement capability. Because of these shortcomings, the M11/39 is often considered one of the least successful Italian tanks of the Second World War.

The M11/39 proved very problematic in terms of reliability and performance, and its limited design and armament limited its operational effectiveness in the wartime context.

Reports of combat actions near Agorat in March 1941 showed that it was relatively easy to incapacitate the crew by shooting at the tank from the sides, exploiting its rear vulnerability due to its limited armour. However, probably its greatest flaw was, as mentioned, the lack of a radio, which limited communication and coordination of operations. The next model, the M13/40, solved both these problems by mounting a 47mm cannon in the turret and providing a radio as standard. The M13/40 was already available when production of the M11/39 was completed and was designed with a more robust design, despite sharing many of the same negative features as the M11/39.

Production of the M11/39 therefore ended with the delivery of the last example in July 1939. Although orders were given for the production of further tanks in 1938, these orders were not officially cancelled until October 1939. In fact, the more advanced M13/40 medium tank was already available at this time and production focused appropriately on this vehicle to meet the needs of the Italian Army. Although one example of the M11/39 was known to have been sent to Britain for evaluation and there are rumours of another being shipped to Australia for display, no M11/39 has survived to this day.

▲ Beautiful picture of an M11/39 operating in A.O.I.

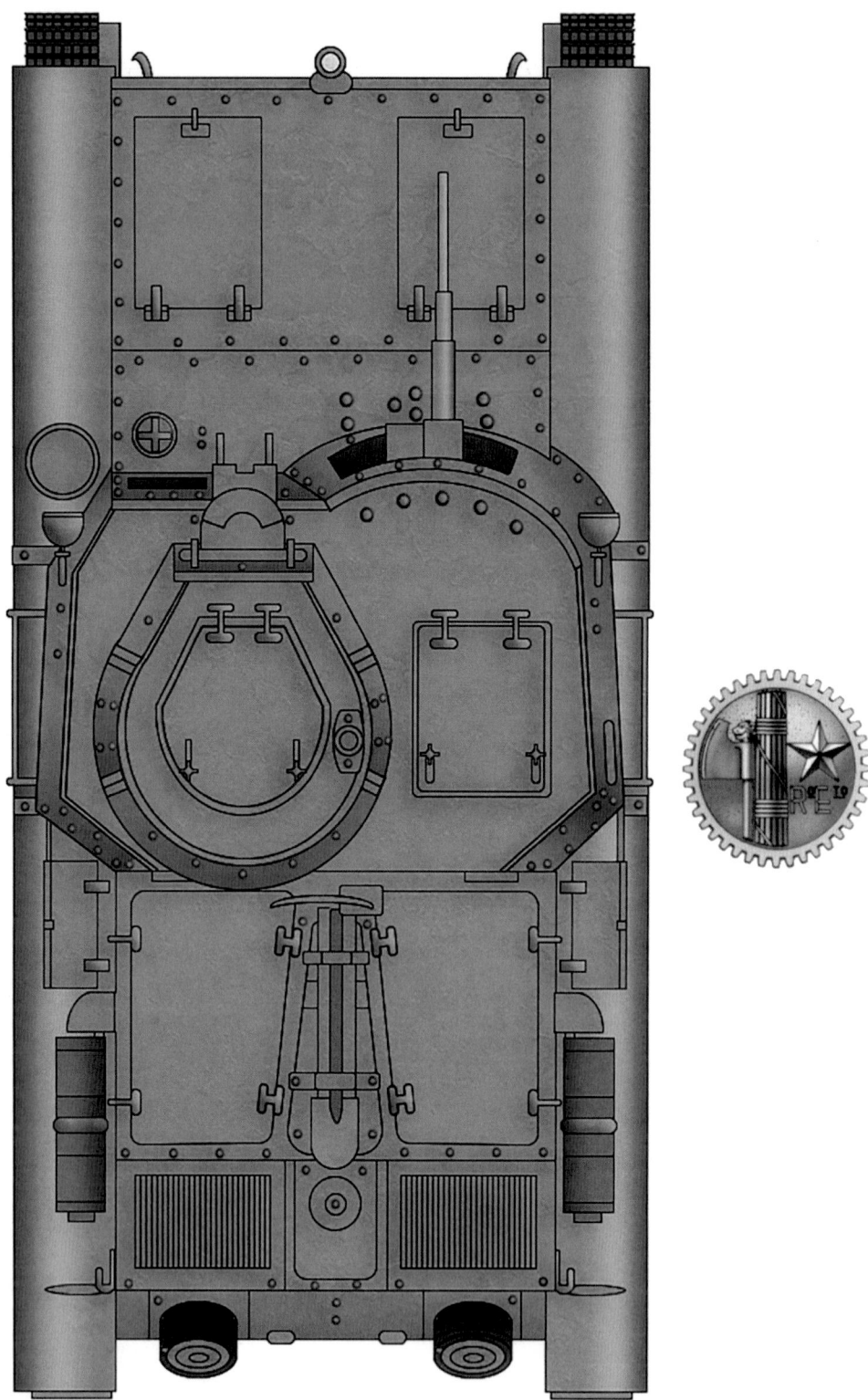

▲ View of the medium Italian tank M11/39 above. On the right, the bronze or aluminium badge was placed on the front plate of Italian armoured vehicles from April 1936 to August 1943.

M11/39 MEDIUM TANK IN EGYPT IN 1940

▲ M11/39 operating in the Sidi el Barrani area, Egypt, September 1940.

▲ Parade of M11 tanks during a military parade in Rome in 1939. State Archives (author's colouring).

▼ Pre-war military exercises of the M11/39 tank on national territory. State Archives.

M11/39 MEDIUM TANK IN EGYPT IN 1940

▲ M11/39 tank, loaded on Viberti trailer for transport. North Africa, 1940.

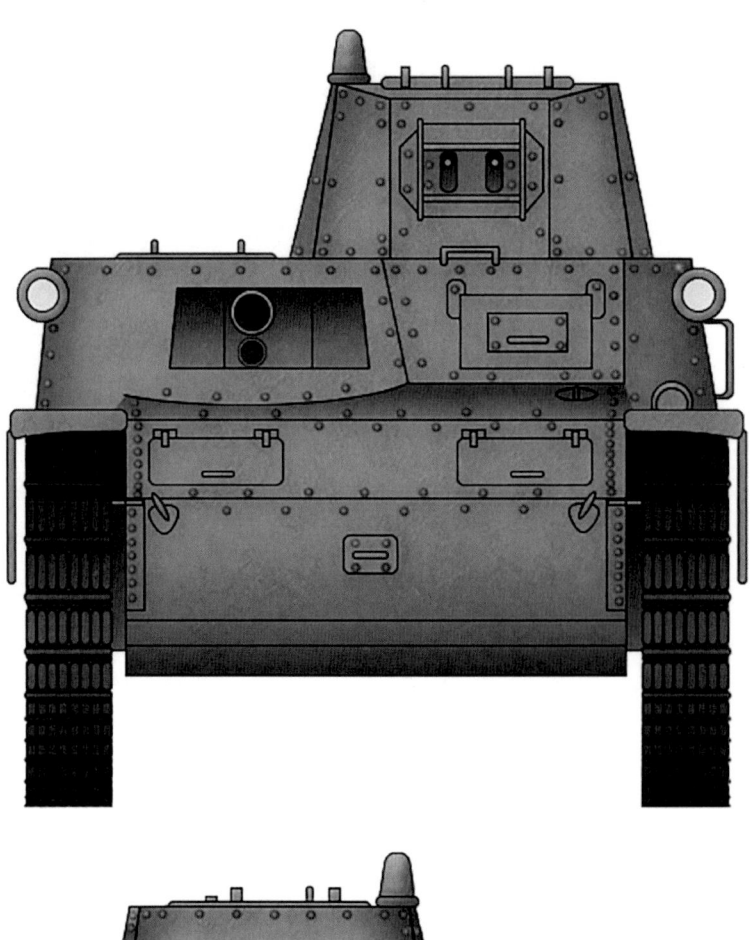

▲ View of the medium Italian tank M11/39 from the front and back.

M11/39 MEDIUM TANK IN SOMALILAND (UK) IN 1940

▲ M11/39 in East Africa, British invasion of Somaliland, September 1940.

M11/39 MEDIUM TANK IN SOMALILAND (UK) IN 1940

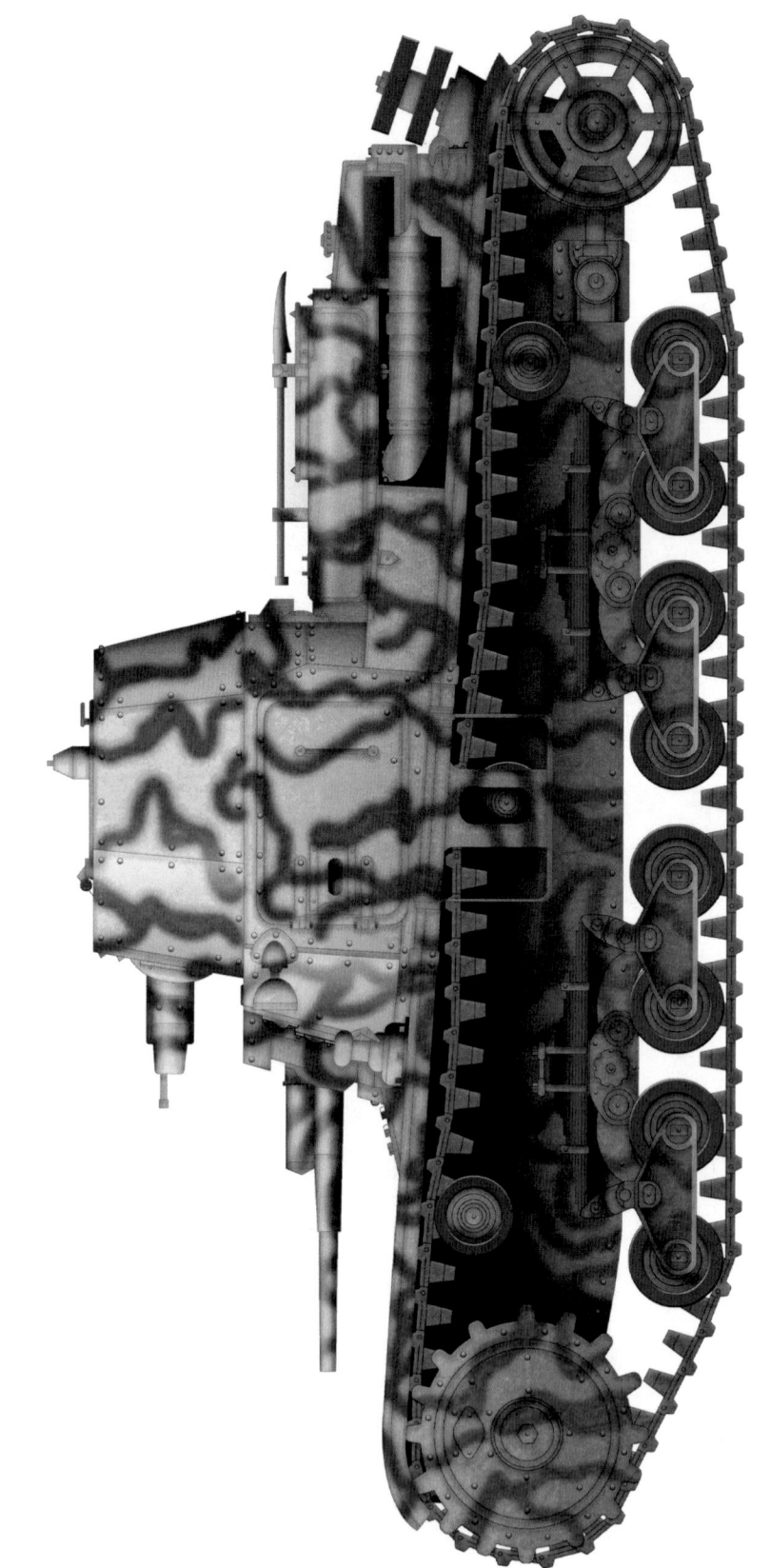

▲ M11/39 used in the early stages of the war for the invasion of British Somaliland in September 1940. Second camouflage version.

CAMOUFLAGE AND DISTINGUISHING MARKS

The background colours of the medium tanks, both M13-14-15 and M11, from their creation until 1945, (the operational period of this use is indicated in brackets) also used for all armoured vehicles were: R.E. grey green (1936-1945), dark chocolate (1936-1941), reddish brown (1936-1943), ochre (for prototypes), sand (1941-1945), dark sand (1943-1945), dark grey (1941-1943). For camouflage, medium green (1936-1943) and dark red (for prototypes) were used.

Medium tanks had not yet emerged at the time of the Ethiopian War 1935-1936 and the Spanish Civil War 1937-1939. *National territory 1936-1940* - substantial predominance of grey-green. Occupation of *Albania and French Front 1939-1940* - grey-green.

Campaign of Greece and Yugoslavia 1940-1941 - grey-green possibly camouflaged with green and sand-coloured flecks. *East Africa 1940-1941* - grey green or in the old Ethiopian campaign camouflage reddish brown with green spots. *North Africa 1940-1943* - at first only green-grey, the colour in which they were generally landed at destination ports, then sand-coloured in various variegated versions. Not used in the Russian Campaign 1941-1943.

France and Corsica 1942 - grey-green and sand with possible reddish-brown patches. *CSR 1943-1945* dark sand grey-green, reddish brown with medium dense green flecks, in uniform German panzer grey colour. In particular, the tanks of the Leonessa and partly also the Leoncello were dark sand in colour. Elaborate camouflage in irregular chequered patterns of sandy yellow background and green and brown patches.

◼ MEDIUM TANK BADGES

In order to recognise individual armoured vehicles in military operations, even for Italy, it became necessary to introduce an identification system, also because, at least initially, there were no tanks with radios installed. In fact, radios only began to be installed with some regularity from 1941 onwards. In the beginning, flags with red or white drapes were used for communication.

The first table of distinctive tank markings dates back to 1925 and was very complex and articulated to excess. Number groups were only introduced in 1927 after the establishment of the Tank Regiment, and new regulations were issued in 1928. In 1940, the first deliveries of M13/40 Tanks finally began, which were distributed to the various armoured divisions.

The Medium tanks, as had already been the case with the Light tanks, bore symbols identified by markings, names and numbers placed on both sides of the hull. The numbers were painted on the front of the hull plate and on both sides.

In 1938, to simplify recognition, a further change was made, this time a radical one: new tactical tank symbols were established. This system was also followed by the medium tanks that came into being a few years later. The tank companies were represented by coloured rectangles as follows:

The first company had the colour red, the 2nd company blue, the 3rd company yellow, the 4th company green; the colour white was reserved for regimental command tanks. The insignia of the tanks and armoured cars had to be 20 x 12 cm in size and painted in the company colour.

The coloured rectangles were cut by white bars (1 to 4 lines and a diagonal for 5th platoon) and indicated the different platoons, full colour and without lines for Company Command tanks.

The rectangles of the various platoons were surmounted by an Arabic number (the colour of the company) indicating the tank in the platoon's organic formation.

These numbers had to be 10 cm high and 1.5 cm thick, and placed in the centre of the upper side of the rectangle 2 cm apart. Below the rectangle the number of the battalion to which it belonged was placed in white Roman numerals. Battalion tanks, if in reserve at Regimental level, instead bore only the relative

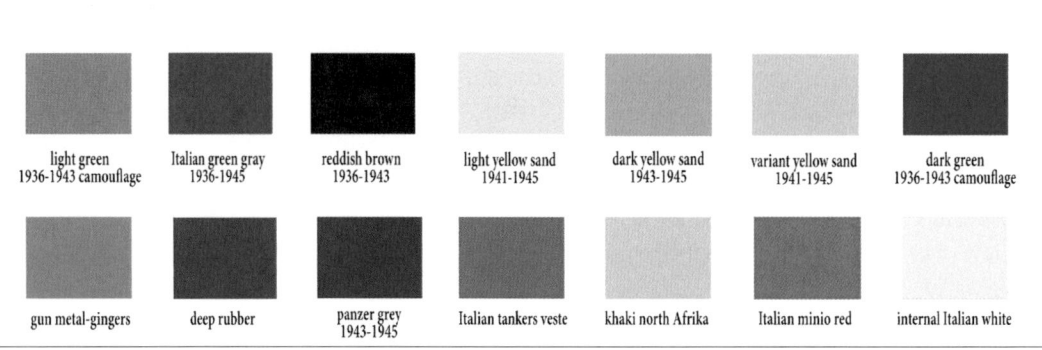

light green 1936-1943 camouflage	Italian green gray 1936-1945	reddish brown 1936-1943	light yellow sand 1941-1945	dark yellow sand 1943-1945	variant yellow sand 1941-1945	dark green 1936-1943 camouflage
gun metal-gingers	deep rubber	panzer grey 1943-1945	Italian tankers veste	khaki north Afrika	Italian minio red	internal Italian white

Arabic number. Battalion command squadron tanks had a completely black rectangle. The battalion command tank on two companies had it half red and half blue on the right. The battalion command tank on three companies had it on three coloured lines from left to right: red, blue and yellow.

Specifically for the medium tanks, the distinctive sign was placed on the turret in the front mid-upper part. At the rear, in the middle part of the turret. On some tanks, the rectangle was placed at the height of the access hatch to the combat chamber. On the same hatch, the distinctive sign of the Division, such as a black ram, often appeared. As an aerial identification sign on the vehicles, a white Savoy cross was sometimes painted in the summer of 1940 and placed, depending on the type of vehicle, on the turret or engine compartment ceiling. From 1941, a white disc 70 cm in diameter was painted instead of the cross. Although the circular clearly stated, there were numerous exceptions and variations to the official regulations.

The medium tanks used by the Italian Social Republic showed the distinguishing marks of the various departments painted on them: the 'Leoncello' was depicted by a black lion clutching a fascio littorio looking to the left on a white background. The 'Leonessa' had a slightly more complicated distinguishing sign formed by the red M of Mussolini, cut by a black fasces and underneath the always black inscription 'GNR'.

Instead of the coloured rectangles, a rectangle of the same size was used with the simple tricolour flag or the republican type with a black eagle in the centre. The numbers both below and above were always white.

The tanks used by the Germans, especially the captured ones, and the new ones ordered after the armistice of 1943 bore the typical German army markings starting with the black and white *ritterkreuz* in its various forms.

▲ An Italian M11/39 tank with the tank commander in the turret in November 1940 on the African front. Model photographed at a competition.

M11/39 MEDIUM TANK IN EGYPT IN 1940

▲ M11/39 2nd M tank battalion of the 'Maletti' column – Italian offensive in September 1940, North Africa. In the small photo the same tank in the Egyptian desert.

▲ M11 tanks and other Italian vehicles near Sollum 1940.

◄ Medium tank with commander leaving the vehicle.

▼ M11/39 tank next to the small light fast tank in the yards of the Ansaldo factory.

M11/39 MEDIUM TANK IN ALBANIA IN 1941

▲ M11/39 in use with the 1st Company 4th Battalion in Albania, spring 1941.

M11/39 MEDIUM TANK IN LIBYA IN 1941

▲ M11/39 operating in Libya in 1941.
In the small photo the same tanks in the North African desert.

PRODUCTION AND EXPORT

Production of the Italian tank began in 1938 at the rate of 9 tanks per month. In December 1939, all Italian medium tank production was concentrated on the M13/40, closing the assembly line of the M11/39, which proved to be a major failure. In total, around 100 M11-39s were produced. Also because of its relative low number, it was essentially an Italian-only vehicle, i.e. used predominantly and almost exclusively by the Royal Army, the main customer.

However, very few of these tanks ended up in enemy hands because they were captured.

• Australia: following the battles in the North African desert, Australian troops took possession of a number of armoured vehicles, mainly M11/39, M13/40 and M14/41. These vehicles were rehabilitated by the Australians themselves and repainted with typical colours and markings (the famous white kangaroos). In the case of the M11/39, there are several photos showing this tank being used in operations around Tobruk.

• Italian Social Republic: After the collapse of Italy following the events of September 8, a new state was created in German-controlled northern Italy. The RSI used many of the military vehicles already belonging to the Regio Esercito at its disposal. Of these, only one M11/39 is known to have been used in Piedmont by some ENR formations in the period between 1943 and 1945. The best known operation involving this tank was the one called 'Nachtigal'. It was almost certainly a vehicle used by the 1ª GNR Frontier Legion in support of the units employed in the anti-Partisan operation on 14 August 1944. The vehicle was one of only four survivors in Italy in September 1943, and was kept at the Italian cavalry school where RSI units took it. It appears that the vehicle was abandoned after the August 1944 action.

• German Army: in the same way, and in a massive and selective manner, the German Army also confiscated and refitted all available Italian vehicles after September 8. In some cases even reactivating the production assembly lines (especially in the case of the M15 and derived self-propelled vehicles). This was not the case for the M11/39 tank, which was considered to be of little value by the Germans. However, pictures are preserved of one of these vehicles, captured and converted with German insignia, and referred to by the new Germanic designation of M11/39 734/i, in the critical Roman days of the armistice in September 1943. There is, in fact, a photo from the Bundesarchiv showing this tank in the hands of German troops running around the Colosseum area in Rome.

▲ Tank of the Maletti Regiment in the Cyrenaica desert. State Archives.

▼ M11/39 tank operating in the Ethiopian theatre (A.O.I.). State Archives.

▲ M11 tank waiting to participate in a military review in Rome in 1939.

▼ M11/39 tank in beautiful camouflage. State Archives.

▲ British soldiers have their picture taken in front of a captured M11/39.

▼ Another image of the tanks captured by the Australians in Africa and framed in the 6th Australian cavalry regiment at Tobruk in April 1941. Note an M13/40 tank in the background.

M11/39 MEDIUM TANK IN SOMALILAND IN 1941

▲ M11/39 in use with the 332nd Company in Somaliland A.O.I. 1941. In the small photo other tanks belonging to the same company.

DATA SHEET

	M11/39
Length	4700 mm
Width	2200 mm
Height	2300 mm
Minimum hull height above ground	0,38 m
Weight in combat order	11.200 kg
Crew	3 (commander/radio operator, driver, gunner)
Engine	Fiat SPA 8T, V8 diesel, 105 hp
Maximum speed	33.9 km/h on-road and 15 km/h off-road
Autonomy	200 km on-road and 120 off-road
Tank capacity	182 L
Armour thickness	6 to 30 mm
Armament	1 37 mm (1.46 inch) Vickers Terni L40 cannon, (84 rounds) Breda 38 8 mm (0.31 inch) twin machine gun, (2,800 rounds)
Production	100 examples

▼ Possible variable of the Australian painting of the M11/39 tank used at Tobruk (see page right).

M11/39 'AUSTRALIAN' MEDIUM TANK AT TOBRUK IN 1941

▲ M11/39 in use by the Australian forces and used by the 6th Australian Division Cavalry Regiment during the assault on Tobruk on 21-22 January 1941 as shown in the small photo in the top corner.

▲ M11/39 tanks in the African desert

▲ The M11/39 tank captured by German troops during the defence of Rome by the Royal Army and immediately reused. Here it appears in movement in the area in front of the Colosseum. Bundesarchiv.

M11/39 MEDIUM TANK IN SOMALILAND IN 1941

▲ M11/39 in use by the South African forces indicated by a large number 1.
In the small photo: the same tank captured by the Italians belonging to the same company.

M11/39 MEDIUM TANK USED BY THE THESSALONIANS, SEPTEMBER 1943 ROME - ITALY

▲ M11/39 captured by German troops intent on suppressing the rebellion of the Italian army following the armistice of 8 September 1943 in Rome.

RSI M11/39 MEDIUM TANK IN PIEDMONT, 1944

▲ M11/39 (hypothetical reconstruction) used in the course of Operation 'Nachtigal'; it was almost certainly a vehicle used by the 1st Frontier GNR Legion in support of the units employed in the anti-Partisan operation on 14 August 1944.

BIBLIOGRAPHY

- *Carro M - carri medi M 11-39, M 13-40, M 14-41, M 15-42, semoventi e altri derivati*, Antonio Tallillo, Andrea Tallillo, Daniele Guglielmi, Gruppo Modellistico Trentino, 2010.
- *Carro M - carri medi M 11-39, M 13-40, M 14-41, M 15-42, semoventi e altri derivati*, Antonio Tallillo, Andrea Tallillo, Daniele Guglielmi, vol. 2 Gruppo Modellistico Trentino, 2012.
- *Veicoli da Combattimento dell'Esercito Italiano dal 1939 al 1945.* Falessi, Cesare; Pafi, Benedetto (1976). Intyrama books.
- *Italian Medium Tanks, 1939–45. New Vanguard 195.* Cappellano, F.; Battistelli, P. P. (2012). Oxford: Osprey Publishing.
- *Italian Armored Vehicles of World War Two.* Pignato, Nicola (2004).Squadron/Signal publications.
- *Carri* armati *medi italiani in azione*, Armor numero 39, Squadron/Signal Publications, Nicola Pignato, 2001
- *Storia dei mezzi corazzati.* Pignato, Nicola. Vol. II. Fratelli Fabbri Editori.
- *I reparti corazzati italiani nei Balcani*, Paolo Crippa e Carlo Cucut. Soldiershop 2019.
- *I reparti corazzati del R.E. E l'armistizio 1° Volume*, Paolo Crippa. Soldiershop 2021.
- *I reparti corazzati del R.E. E l'armistizio 2° Volume*, Paolo Crippa. Soldiershop 2021.
- *Il gruppo corazzato del Leoncello*, Paolo Crippa. Soldiershop 2021.
- *I mezzi blindo-corazzati italiani 1923-1943*, Nicola Pignato, Storia Militare, 2005.
- *Gli autoveicoli da combattimento dell'Esercito Italiano, Volume secondo (1940-1945)*, Stato Maggiore dell'Esercito, Ufficio Storico, Nicola Pignato e Filippo Cappellano, 2002.
- *Carri armati e autoblindate del Regio esercito italiano 1918-1943.* Giulio Benussi. Intergest 1973
- *Mezzi dell'Esercito Italiano 1935-45*, Ugo Barlozzetti & Alberto Pirella, Editoriale Olimpia, 1986.
- *Corazzati e blindati italiani dalle origini allo scoppio della seconda guerra mondiale*, David Vannucci, Editrice Innocenti, 2003.
- *"L'Ariete a Bir-El Gobi". Storia Militare (in Italian).* Maraziti, Antonio (Gennaio 2005). Albertelli edizioni.
- *Italian Medium Tanks in Action*, Nicola Pignato, 2001.
- *Carro armato M* Ufficio autonomo degli approvvigionamenti automobolistici. *Regio esercito* 1939.
- *Il gruppo corazzato "San Giusto" dal Regio Esercito alla RSI 1934-1945*, Stefano Di Giusto, Laran Éditions, 2008.
- *I reparti corazzati della Repubblica Sociale Italiana 1943/1945*, Paolo Crippa, Marvia Edizioni, 2006.
- *Alle origini della Breda Meccanica Bresciana*, A. Curami, P. Ferrari & A. Rastelli, Fondazione Negri, 2009.
- *Storia dell'Ansaldo 6. Dall'IRI alla guerra 1930-1945*, Gabriele De Rosa, Gius. Laterza & Figli, 1999.

BOOKS ALREADY PUBLISHED

THE WEAPONS ENCYCLOPÆDIA
TANK AIRCRAFT AFV SHIP ARTILLERY VEHICLES SECRET WEAPON

I CARRI LEGGERI CV L3/33-35-38

COLLANA CURATA DA LUCA CRISTINI

THE WEAPONS ENCYCLOPÆDIA
TANK AIRCRAFT AFV SHIP ARTILLERY VEHICLES SECRET WEAPON

FOCKE-WULF FW 190

SERIES EDITED BY LUCA CRISTINI

THE WEAPONS ENCYCLOPÆDIA
TANK AIRCRAFT AFV SHIP ARTILLERY VEHICLES SECRET WEAPON

SEMOVENTE 75/18 & 75/34

SERIES EDITED BY LUCA CRISTINI

THE WEAPONS ENCYCLOPÆDIA
TANK AIRCRAFT AFV SHIP ARTILLERY VEHICLES SECRET WEAPON

CARRO MEDIO ITALIANO M13-40, M14-41 & M15-42

COLLANA CURATA DA LUCA CRISTINI

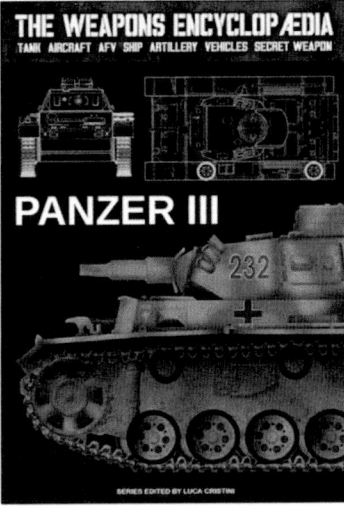

THE WEAPONS ENCYCLOPÆDIA
TANK AIRCRAFT AFV SHIP ARTILLERY VEHICLES SECRET WEAPON

PANZER III

SERIES EDITED BY LUCA CRISTINI

THE WEAPONS ENCYCLOPÆDIA
TANK AIRCRAFT AFV SHIP ARTILLERY VEHICLES SECRET WEAPON

CANNONI ITALIANI 1914-1945 Vol.1
65/17, 75/13, 75/27, 105/32 & 149/35

COLLANA CURATA DA LUCA CRISTINI

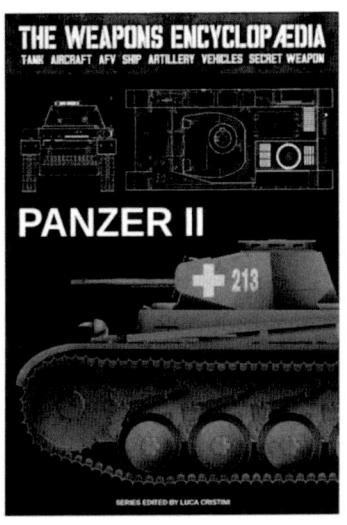

THE WEAPONS ENCYCLOPÆDIA
TANK AIRCRAFT AFV SHIP ARTILLERY VEHICLES SECRET WEAPON

PANZER II

SERIES EDITED BY LUCA CRISTINI

THE WEAPONS ENCYCLOPÆDIA
TANK AIRCRAFT AFV SHIP ARTILLERY VEHICLES SECRET WEAPON

SOMUA S35

COLLANA CURATA DA LUCA CRISTINI

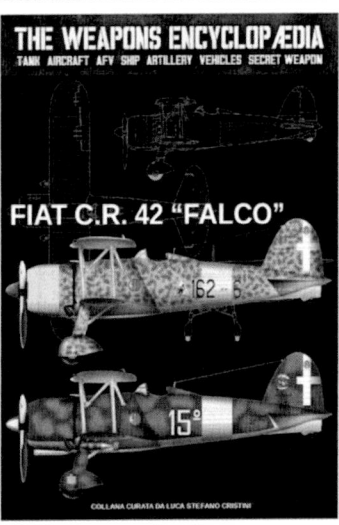

THE WEAPONS ENCYCLOPÆDIA
TANK AIRCRAFT AFV SHIP ARTILLERY VEHICLES SECRET WEAPON

FIAT C.R. 42 "FALCO"

COLLANA CURATA DA LUCA STEFANO CRISTINI

SOLDIERSHOP PUBLISHING
ILLUSTRATED HISTORY
TWE-012 EN